DOMINOES

Conan the Barbarian:
The Jewels of Gwahlur

Robert E. Howard

Founder Editors: Bill Bowler and Sue Parminter

Text adaptation by Bill Bowler

Illustrated by Ollie Cuthbertson

Robert Ervin Howard (1906-1936) was an American author of popular fiction. He wrote different kinds of stories, and many of these were published in famous fiction magazines such as *Weird Tales*. His work includes fantasy stories, cowboy stories, and sports stories. Conan the Barbarian is Howard's most famous character, and there have been a number of Conan films.

OXFORD
UNIVERSITY PRESS

Great Clarendon Street, Oxford, OX2 6DP, United Kingdom

Oxford University Press is a department of the University of Oxford.
It furthers the University's objective of excellence in research, scholarship,
and education by publishing worldwide. Oxford is a registered trade
mark of Oxford University Press in the UK and in certain other countries

ISBN: 978 0 19 424566 1   Book
ISBN: 978 0 19 463958 3   Book and Audio Pack

Printed in China

This book is printed on paper from certified and well-managed sources

ACKNOWLEDGEMENTS

Cover image: Ollie Cuthbertson/Bright Agency

*The author and series editor wish to express their thanks to Hardy Griffin for his helpful comments on
the story.*

Illustrations by: Ollie Cuthbertson/Bright Agency

The publisher would like to thank the following for permission to reproduce photographs: Alamy
Images pp.18 (The Sof Omar cave system/Michael Runkel Ethiopia), 56 (John Lackland
King of England/North Wind Picture Archives), 57 (President Paul Kruger/The Art Archive);
Getty Images pp.7 (Rainforest/Travelpix Ltd), 19 (Cloudforest vegetation, Montverde
Reserve/Art Wolfe); Shutterstock p.60 (Ta Phrom temple/Kjersti Joergensen)

Contents

BEFORE READING

1 **Here are some of the people in *Conan the Barbarian: The Jewels of Gwahlur*. Match each sentence with a picture. Use a dictionary to help you.**

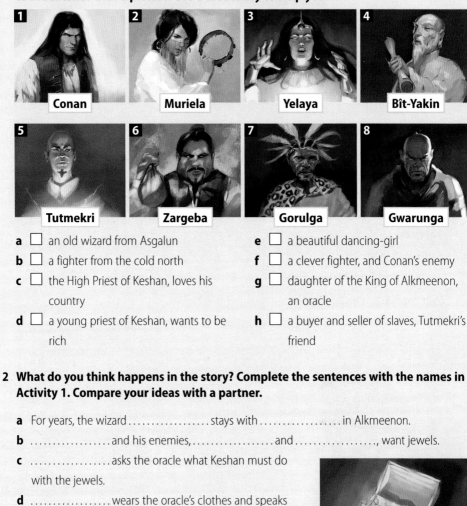

1 Conan	2 Muriela	3 Yelaya	4 Bît-Yakin

5 Tutmekri	6 Zargeba	7 Gorulga	8 Gwarunga

a ☐ an old wizard from Asgalun

b ☐ a fighter from the cold north

c ☐ the High Priest of Keshan, loves his country

d ☐ a young priest of Keshan, wants to be rich

e ☐ a beautiful dancing-girl

f ☐ a clever fighter, and Conan's enemy

g ☐ daughter of the King of Alkmeenon, an oracle

h ☐ a buyer and seller of slaves, Tutmekri's friend

2 **What do you think happens in the story? Complete the sentences with the names in Activity 1. Compare your ideas with a partner.**

a For years, the wizard . . . . stays with . . . . in Alkmeenon.

b . . . . and his enemies, ... and . . . . , want jewels.

c . . . . asks the oracle what Keshan must do with the jewels.

d . . . . wears the oracle's clothes and speaks in her place.

e . . . . helps the jewel-thieves for money.

3 **Who do you think has the jewels in the end?**

a ☐ Conan   **b** ☐ Conan's enemies   **c** ☐ nobody

CHAPTER ONE
On the Cliffs of Alkmeenon

The sun was coming up. Its red, early-morning light touched the high wall of blue stone. The blue **cliff** began deep in the **jungle** below. Was it possible to climb to the top of it? Wasn't it too high? But a man wearing bright red clothes was slowly moving up it. He was climbing like a big jungle cat, and he was more than half of the way up. His hair was long and dark. He had the strong body of a climber, and he wore nothing on his feet. He came from the hills of the cold north, but now he was far from home in the hot south. His shoes were on his back, out of the way. And his knife and **sword** were beside him. It was Conan the **Barbarian**!

Just then, Conan saw a small **cave** mouth in the face of the cliff above him. He climbed up into the cave to rest. But it was not deep, and it was not empty. The dead body of an old man sat against the back wall. His yellow clothes were full of holes, and his face and hands were brown and dry from hundreds of years of mountain wind.

cliff a high wall of stone

jungle a place in a hot country with a lot of trees

sword a long, sharp knife for fighting

barbarian someone wild who comes from a wild country

cave a hole in the side of a cliff

The **mummy** held an old letter in its thin fingers. Conan took this from the mummy. Without opening it, he put it in his **belt**. Then he climbed out of the cave, and went on up the cliff.

Soon after that, he arrived at the top, and looked over the other side. The blue cliffs made a circle of high, stone walls around a secret **valley**. There was a green jungle at the bottom of this circular valley, but it was thinner than the jungle outside the cliffs. Between the tops of the green trees, Conan could see wonderful, old buildings of white stone.

'The great **city** of Alkmeenon!' he cried. 'Famous for the rich people who lived here once. Somewhere in this valley they've hidden the **Jewels** of Gwahlur, and I'm going to find them!'

*That was why Conan came south to the country of Keshan many months before. That was why he decided to stay and help the **King** of Keshan. That was why he began teaching the army of Keshan better ways of fighting against their great enemies, the people of Punt. It was all because he wanted to steal the Jewels of **Gwahlur**.*

Then one day Tutmekri came to Keshan. Tutmekri was a fighter like Conan. More importantly, he was a past enemy of Conan's. Tutmekri was now working for the King of Zembabwei. He came – with his

mummy the dry body of a dead person that cold winds have kept whole

belt you wear this round your middle

valley land between hills or cliffs

city (*plural* **cities**) a big and important town

jewel an expensive stone

king the most important man in a country

Gwahlur /ˈghwælɜr/

friend and **ally Zargeba** – to speak with the King of Keshan. Conan could not stop these two visitors from talking to the king. So he followed and stayed near them, listening carefully to what they said.

'King of Keshan,' began Tutmekri. 'Do you need help to fight against the men of Punt? Punt has now started fighting Zembabwei. So the King of Zembabwei would like to be your ally. Zembabwei is a strong country, and your enemies are our enemies. Together we can easily win the fight. I and Zargeba both have great armies of soldiers who work for us. They can fight for you. After we win, Keshan can have the west of Punt, and Zembabwei can take the east. Our two countries will be rich and happy.'

'What will it cost to have your help?' asked the King of Keshan.

'Zembabwei wants to be the only country that can buy gold, silver, and other expensive things in Keshan's great city market. And the King of Zembabwei would like some of the Jewels of Gwahlur. He asks – as a brother – for this present from his new ally. But do not worry. He will put the Jewels in the great **temple** of Zembabwei because they belong in a special place.'

ally (*plural* **allies**) a person that is on your side and helps you in a fight

Zargeba /ˈzɑːɡeɪbæ/

temple some people go here to speak to their gods

Conan smiled at these false words. He said nothing. He knew that it would do no good. He saw that he needed to move quickly and steal the Jewels of Gwahlur soon, before Tutmekri or his friend Zargeba could get them. But where in Keshan were those expensive stones? After months of looking for them, he still didn't know.

Then the **High Priest**, Gorulga, spoke. 'Before we can agree to this, I must ask the **oracle** in the old city of Alkmeenon what to do. I will go to her tomorrow. If great Yelaya says "yes" to this plan, we will bring the jewels from Alkmeenon to Keshan. We will send some of them to our new allies. But if she tells us "no", Tutmekri must go back to Zembabwei with empty hands.'

Everybody began talking excitedly at this news.

'Who is Yelaya?' asked Tutmekri.

'She was the daughter of a King of Alkmeenon hundreds of years ago,' answered a tall **priest** at Gorulga's side. 'She died when she was young and beautiful. After that, all the people of Alkmeenon left the city. They found new homes here in Keshan.'

high priest the most important man who works in a temple

oracle a woman who can see things before they happen, and answer people's difficult questions cleverly

priest a man who works in a temple

4

'Yelaya's dead body stayed young and beautiful for hundreds of years,' explained the king, 'Soon priests from Keshan began visiting the empty city to ask her important questions, and she gave them answers. They began to call her the Oracle.'

The king's wife went on with the story: 'But the last priest to visit Alkmeenon, over a hundred years ago now, was a criminal. He tried to steal the Jewels of Gwahlur for himself, and he died a most terrible death for this crime. His followers hurried from Alkmeenon, and escaped back to Keshan. But they never described what they saw in the dead city. They were too afraid to speak of it to anyone. Since that time, no priest has visited the Oracle of Alkmeenon...'

Conan left the room quietly. If the jewels were somewhere in Alkmeenon, he needed to find them before Gorulga got there. He decided to go through the jungle and climb over the cliffs to arrive in Yelaya's city before the High Priest. 'Gorulga is an old man,' thought Conan. 'He'll take the long, open road to Alkmeenon. I've learned about a secret door from people here – it's at the foot of the cliffs in the south. He'll go into the valley through it. All of this will take a long time. I can get there much more quickly.'

Conan left the city of Keshan that afternoon, and walked straight into the jungle.

The barbarian began to climb down the inside of the cliff wall. 'Why did everybody leave Alkmeenon all those years ago?' he asked himself. 'Did many people in the city fall ill and die? Were they afraid of something?' One thing was sure. Conan knew that he was here before Gorulga and his priests. He walked through the trees and across the valley floor to the city of the Oracle Yelaya, the city that held the Jewels of Gwahlur. Could he steal those jewels before the High Priest Gorulga took them back to Keshan, and gave a handful of them to Tutmekri?

READING CHECK

1 Are these sentences true or false? Tick the boxes.

		True	False
a	Conan is travelling to Alkmeenon when the story begins.	☑	☐
b	Conan wants the Jewels of Gwahlur for himself.	☐	☐
c	Tutmekri asks for some money for the King of Zembabwei.	☐	☐
d	Gorulga wants to ask Yelaya about the jewels.	☐	☐
e	Yelaya is the Oracle of Zembabwei.	☐	☐
f	Nobody has visited Yelaya for many years.	☐	☐
g	The last person to visit Alkmeenon died a terrible death.	☐	☐
h	Conan wants to visit Alkmeenon after Gorulga.	☐	☐
i	Conan finds an old man's body in the jungle.	☐	☐
j	Conan reads the old man's letter, but takes it with him.	☐	☐

2 Use the place names on the map to complete the text.

Conan is working for the King of
a) ...Keshan... . Tutmekri
is working for the King of
b) ....
c) .... is the enemy
of both countries, so Tutmekri
says that **d)** ....
and **e)** .... can be
allies. Together the two of them
can fight against the people of
f) .... After they win
the fight, **g)** .... can take
the west of their enemies' country and
h) .... can take the east.

WORD WORK

Use the words in the jungle to complete the sentences.

a Gorulga, Gwarunga, and other priests work in the ....temple.... of Keshan.

b Keshan and Alkmeenon are the names of two .... in Conan's world.

c Alkmeenon is in the middle of a big, circular ....

d There's a high wall of blue .... all round Alkmeenon.

e The King of Keshan needs .... to help him fight against Punt.

f Conan goes into a .... to rest, and finds a dead old man there.

g The old man died years earlier, and his body has become a ....

h Conan puts the old man's letter in his ....

i Conan's .... and knife are on his back, out of the way.

j Conan is a wild .... from the north.

GUESS WHAT

Which of these things do you think happen in the next chapter? Tick three boxes.

a ☐ Conan finds the Jewels of Gwahlur.

b ☐ Conan finds the Oracle of Alkmeenon.

c ☐ Yelaya speaks to Conan.

d ☐ Conan reads the letter, and learns who the old man was.

e ☐ A strange sound tells Conan that he is not alone in Alkmeenon.

f ☐ Conan meets Tutmekri and fights him.

CHAPTER TWO
Where are the Jewels?

With his soft shoes now on his feet, Conan climbed the white stone stairs to the **palace**. It was the biggest, most beautiful building in Alkmeenon. He went quietly inside. His knife was in his belt, and his sword was in his hand. The palace was silent.

Conan moved carefully down a long, dark **corridor**. At the end of this, two large **metal** doors stood open. He walked between them into a large **hall**. Light came in from small windows in the high **ceiling**. At the far end of the hall, there was a white stone **dais**. A beautiful gold chair stood on this dais. Conan's face brightened. 'The gold **throne** of Alkmeenon!' he said softly to himself. Conan was always looking for something expensive that he could steal. But he knew that even he couldn't carry the great throne away. It was too heavy.

Conan looked around the large hall. 'Why isn't Yelaya on the throne? Was the oracle ever really here?' he asked himself. 'Or... wait... **maybe** she's somewhere near the throne room.'

There was a small open **doorway** behind the throne. Conan walked over and looked through this. He saw a narrow corridor going off to one side. Then he saw another doorway, with a beautiful gold door, in the wall to the left of the throne. He went over and touched the door. It opened easily, and he walked inside.

He found himself in a square room with walls of white stone, and a high gold ceiling. The doorway behind him was the only way in, and there was a narrow **ivory** dais on one side of the room. The oracle was lying on this cold, hard bed. Yelaya was many hundreds of years old, but her body was no dry, old mummy. She was still young and coldly beautiful, even in death. How was that possible?

palace a big house where a king lives with his family

corridor you can walk from room to room in a building along this

metal gold and silver are expensive metals

hall a big room in the middle of a palace

ceiling the part of a room above your head

dais a part of the floor of a room which is higher than the rest; kings usually sit or stand on this

throne the chair where a king sits

maybe perhaps

doorway a hole in the wall of a building where a door can go

ivory this is white, and hard, and comes from the long tusks on an elephant's face

'**Magic**!' thought Conan. Even the oracle's gold shoes and belt, and her fine white dress, were bright and new. The jewels in her hair, around her neck, and in her belt were full of light.

Conan remembered why he was in Alkmeenon. 'The Jewels of Gwahlur! But where are they?' he thought. 'Hmm, maybe they hid them inside the oracle's bed.' He knocked the ivory dais with his sword and listened carefully. It was **solid**. Then he went back into the throne room. He knocked the dais under the throne with his sword. It was solid, too.

magic
something that makes things happen in a way that you can't understand

solid with no empty space inside

9

'Gorulga will be here this evening with his priests. I must find those jewels before they arrive!'

Conan thought darkly of Tutmekri's clever plan. 'I know that my old enemy wants the Jewels of Gwahlur for himself. First, he and his friend Zargeba will take a few of the jewels back to the King of Zembabwei. The king will know then that they're real, and not just an old story. After that, Zembabwei and Keshan will fight against Punt, and win. But the soldiers of Keshan will have to fight hard, and the King of Zembabwei's army will be lazy. Once Zembabwei has half of Punt, its army will start fighting strongly – against the tired soldiers of Keshan! Then Tutmekri's mercenaries will take Keshan, and he'll steal the rest of the Jewels of Gwahlur from the temple there. And if Zargeba tries to stop him, Tutmekri will put a knife in his old friend's back.'

Conan walked through the doorway behind the throne, and along the narrow corridor. But this just finished in a wall with an empty alcove. Then he saw a thin black **crack** between the white stones at the back of the **alcove**. He put his knife into this. At once, a small secret door opened in it. Behind this, there were little holes that went through into the oracle room.

'Of course!' cried Conan. 'When Gorulga questions the oracle, one of his priests will secretly come here, and answer for Yelaya. He'll tell Gorulga – in Yelaya's voice – to agree to Tutmekri's plan. My old enemy paid the High Priest to help him! And the false oracle will surely speak out against me, too. I'll need to leave Keshan in a hurry if I want to stay alive!'

Just then, Conan remembered the old letter that he took from the mummy in the cave. He pulled it from his belt, opened it, and read it. After all his journeys to different countries, the barbarian knew many languages. So he understood it well.

crack a long, thin hole between two things

alcove a small part of a wall that is further back than the rest of the wall

*My name is Bît-Yakin. I am a **wizard** from the city of Asgalun. I came to Alkmeenon many years ago to work for the oracle. Now I am old, and dying. After my death, my **servants** will take my body and leave it in a cave high in the blue cliff wall that stands around Alkmeenon. I will rest there for all time.*

Conan put the letter back in his belt, and thought for a while. 'So the mummy in the cave was an old wizard. I was right! Yelaya's still so young and beautiful because Bît-Yakin used magic on her. But it's strange that no one ever talks of a wizard living in Alkmeenon. They only speak of an empty city. Maybe nobody knew that the old man was here. And where did Bît-Yakin's servants go after they left him?'

Suddenly, the loud noise of a **gong** shook the silent city. Conan was not alone there. 'Are Gorulga and his priests here already?' he thought. 'No! That's not possible! So who – or what – is with me in Alkmeenon?'

wizard a man who makes things happen in a way that you don't understand

servant a person who works for someone

gong a round, hanging metal plate that you hit to make a loud noise

READING CHECK

Put these sentences in the correct order. Number them 1–10.

Conan…

a ☐ finds the oracle on her bed, still young and beautiful.

b ☐ goes into the palace of Alkmeenon.

c ☐ sees the gold throne of Alkmeenon.

d ☐ opens the gold door to the oracle room.

e ☐ finds holes in the alcove behind the throne.

f ☐ sees Yelaya's jewels, and remembers the Jewels of Gwahlur.

g ☐ hits the bed and the dais under the throne with his sword.

h ☐ hears the sound of a gong in the empty city.

i ☐ learns that Bît-Yakin and his servants worked for Yelaya.

j ☐ takes the wizard's letter from his belt and reads it.

WORD WORK

Use the clues to complete the crossword on page 13 with new words from Chapter 2.

DOWN

a A king lives here.

b Perhaps.

c With no hole in the middle.

e You walk from room to room along this.

f You hit this big, round plate to make a noise.

g This is a long, thin hole between two things.

h This part of a floor is higher than the rest.

ACROSS

b Gold and silver are this.

d This part of a wall is further back than the rest.

e This is over your head in a room.

i This is white and hard. It comes from India or Africa.

j This makes things happen in a way that you can't understand.

k A door goes here.

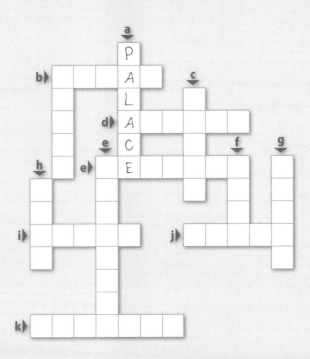

GUESS WHAT

What do you think happens in the next chapter? Tick a box to finish each sentence.

a Conan meets…
- **1** ☐ Bît-Yakin's servants.
- **2** ☐ Muriela, the dancing-girl.
- **3** ☐ Tutmekri's friend, Zargeba.

b Conan falls…
- **1** ☐ and breaks his arm.
- **2** ☐ down some old stairs.
- **3** ☐ into a dark river.

c Conan must…
- **1** ☐ swim and climb for his life.
- **2** ☐ fight and kill Zargeba.
- **3** ☐ leave Alkmeenon with Yelaya.

CHAPTER THREE
The Oracle Speaks

The loud noise of the gong rang through the empty rooms and corridors of the silent palace. The sound surprised Conan, but he was not afraid. He left the throne room, and went after the sound. He ran down the dark corridor, and hurried out of a doorway into a small **courtyard**. Here he saw a large, gold arm coming out of an old, stone wall. **Hanging** from this, there was a great gold gong. It was still moving. And lying under it, on the white stone floor, he saw a gold stick.

'Somebody used that stick to hit the gong! But why?' he asked himself. He looked around, ready for a fight. But nothing moved – everything was silent. Then a strong, animal smell **reached** his nose. It came from near the gong. 'Strange! What is it? No animal that I've ever met!' thought Conan. He moved nearer to find out more.

Just then, the old stone floor under his feet started breaking. Suddenly Conan was falling down through a hole that opened under him. When he put out his hands to stop himself, the stones that he touched broke into little pieces. With an angry cry, he fell heavily down into a deep river that **flowed** below the courtyard. Its waters were dark and cold, and they were flowing fast. The river quickly carried him away, down a **tunnel** that was as black as night.

At first, Conan just tried to keep his head above the water. He didn't fight against the flow or try to swim back. He tried to see where he was going – and what he saw gave him hope. The river was taking him to a place where gray light came down from a large hole in the tunnel ceiling. By this light, Conan could see a high **ledge** that went along one side of the tunnel. From this ledge, a number of old metal **ladders** were hanging down. The bottoms of the ladders nearly touched the water. He

courtyard a place in the middle of a building that is open to the sky

hang (*past* **hung**) to have one end fixed to something, leaving the other end free

reach to arrive at

flow to move in one direction; when water moves in one direction

tunnel a long hole which goes under or through something

ledge a long, flat thing that is high up on a wall, where you can stand or walk

ladder you use this for climbing up and down high things

could escape that way! Before the waters carried him past, he swam strongly to the nearest ladder. It wasn't easy, but at last he reached it. Pulling himself out of the water, he climbed up the ladder. Then he walked along the narrow ledge to the hole in the ceiling. Were the stones around it solid? He touched them to find out. They didn't move. So he quickly pulled himself up out of the hole, and looked around. He was in a large room that was once beautiful but was now old and dirty. 'I'm still in the palace,' he thought. 'Was my fall into the river an accident? I don't think so. Someone – or something – in this city wants to kill me. They knew that the floor wasn't strong. But why were those ladders hanging down over the river?' Conan could not answer that question. So he began walking, looking for the throne room.

At last he found the throne room, and went back into the oracle room. He wanted to look at Yelaya again. He saw the bed of ivory, and the woman on it. She lay in her white dress and her gold shoes, just like before. But when Conan went nearer, he saw something different about her. Earlier she was cold, hard, and dead. But now she was a warm, soft, living woman.

'By all that's good! She's alive!' cried Conan.

Just then, the woman opened her eyes and sat up.

'Yelaya?' asked the barbarian quietly.

'Yes. I am Yelaya, daughter of the King of Alkmeenon,' she replied in a strong, deep voice. 'But what are you doing here? You must leave! Go now!' She **pointed** angrily to the door, but Conan did not move.

point to show something with your finger

'Do not worry,' she said, more softly now. 'I will not hurt you if you leave at once!'

Conan looked at her carefully for a few seconds. Then he laughed. 'You call yourself a king's daughter?' he said. 'Oh, please! I remember you. You're only a poor dancing-girl. Your name's **Muriela**. A year ago, I was in Corinthia and I saw you there – in the **slave** market. Zargeba bought you. How could I forget your face? Also, the way that you speak is really Corinthian!'

'All right. It's true. I am Muriela!' said the slave-girl.

'And why are you here in Alkmeenon?' Conan asked.

'Zargeba brought me,' Muriela explained. 'He and his friend Tutmekri made a secret plan before they arrived in Keshan. Bringing me here was part of that plan – they wanted me to take Yelaya's place!'

'But how did you reach Alkmeenon so fast?' asked Conan.

'Zargeba was in Keshan when I left two days ago. This morning, I climbed up over the cliff wall in the east. What about you?'

'The night after you left, the tall priest, Gwarunga, came alone to Zargeba. They talked about how to find the secret priests' tunnel. It goes under the cliffs in the south. Zargeba left Keshan late that night to find it, and he brought me with him.'

'Ah, so Gwarunga helped you,' said Conan. 'Interesting. Is the High Priest a **traitor** to Keshan, and Tutmekri's ally? Did he send Gwarunga to speak with Zargeba? Or is Gwarunga the traitor priest, working alone? But where's Zargeba?'

Muriela was suddenly worried. 'Oh, no! He'll kill me when he finds out that I've spoken to you!' she cried.

'Is he still in Alkmeenon?' asked Conan.

'Yes. He went outside the palace to wait for the priests,' answered Muriela. 'He's watching the road that they'll take. When they begin arriving, he'll come back to tell me!'

Muriela
/'mjʊərɪəlæ/

slave a person who must work for no money

traitor a person who works against his king, or country

READING CHECK

Correct the mistakes in the sentences.

a Conan finds the gong and a ~~silver~~ gold stick in a courtyard.

b He smells a strong, flowery smell by the gong.

c The floor breaks under him, and he falls into a room under the ground.

d He climbs up an old tree, and along a ledge to escape.

e He goes through a hole in the ceiling, and is back in the jungle again.

f He loses his way back to the oracle room.

g He finds the beautiful woman on her ivory throne – alive!

h The oracle tells Conan to leave Keshan at once.

i Conan understands that she is Yelaya.

j Muriela tells Conan that Tutmekri brought her to Alkmeenon.

k She says that Gorulga helped them to find the way into the valley.

l Muriela thinks that Zargeba will be bored with her, and she is worried.

m She says that Zargeba is waiting for the priests inside the palace.

WORD WORK

1 Find eight more new words from Chapter 3 in the river water.

point ladder courtyard reach traitor slave flow tunnel ledge

2 Complete the sentences with the words from Activity 1 in the correct form.

a Muriela looked at Conan and …pointed… with one finger to the door.

b Some rivers move fast, but others .... more slowly.

c It isn't easy to go along a narrow .... high up on a wall.

d We can walk through one of the .... under the ground.

e He swam quickly across the river until he .... the other side.

f I can climb up one of those old metal .... and escape that way.

g Is Gwarunga working for his king and his country, or is he a .... ?

h Zargeba bought Muriela at the market as a ....

i In the middle of the building there is a .... that is open to the sky.

GUESS WHAT

Which of these things do you think happen in the next chapter? Write Yes or No.

a Muriela goes with Conan into the palace gardens. ....

b Conan leaves Muriela in the oracle room. ....

c Conan kills Zargeba. ....

d Conan finds Zargeba's dead body under some trees. ....

e The priests from Keshan arrive. ....

f Tutmekri meets Zargeba. ....

CHAPTER FOUR

A Strange Flower

Conan looked at Muriela's worried face.

'How long have you been here?' he asked.

'Two hours, maybe,' she answered. 'At first, Zargeba hid me in the middle of some trees outside the palace. He went to find the oracle room. While he was inside, I thought that I heard a gong, but I wasn't sure.'

god an important being who never dies, and who decides what happens in the world

'A gong, eh? Maybe Zargeba hit it,' said Conan. 'Tell me more.'

Muriela went on: 'Then Zargeba brought me here. He took the clothes and jewels from the oracle, and gave them to me. He hid Yelaya's body, while I dressed myself as her. It was all part of the plan.'

'I see,' said Conan. 'And what did Zargeba tell you to do as the oracle?'

Muriela explained. 'When the priests arrived, I had to say that Tutmekri's plan pleased the **gods**. I had to tell Gorulga to take the Jewels of Gwahlur back to Keshan. I had to say that the King of Keshan must give some of the jewels to Tutmekri, and then Tutmekri would take them as a present to the King of Zembabwei. Oh, and I had to say that Conan the Barbarian was a traitor, and must die a traitor's death!'

'Aha! So Gorulga isn't working for Tutmekri!' cried Conan.

'No. He really **trusts** the oracle. That's why Zargeba took me secretly to Keshan. That's why he brought me here, dressed me as Yelaya, and told me what I had to say. It was the only way that Gorulga would agree to Tutkmekri's plan!'

'Then Zargeba left you while he went to watch for the priests.'

'That's right,' said Muriela. 'And I was alone. I closed my eyes, and lay on the ivory bed. But then I began to hear things moving softly around me. I felt afraid. When you arrived, I watched you through half-open eyes. I wanted to ask for help. But then I thought of Zargeba, and how angry he would be. So, as Yelaya the Oracle, I tried to send you away.'

'Until I remembered Corinthia, and understood that you were really Muriela!' laughed the barbarian.

'Yes, you didn't forget me. I was lucky!' Muriela laughed. 'Listen, Conan: I've told you everything that I know because I want to help you. Now you must help me. Zargeba will kill me if you don't stop him!'

'Tell me where he is,' said Conan.

'There's a **thicket** of **lotus** trees by the old road in front of the palace,' explained Muriela quickly. 'This road comes from the cliffs in the south. It's the road that we used. It's the road that the priests are taking. Zargeba's hiding in the trees. Find him and kill him for me!'

'And if I do, will you do something for me?'

'Anything! Just say what.'

'When the priests come, you'll speak to them as the Oracle Yelaya. But you'll say that Tutmekri and Zargeba are traitors. Explain that they want to steal the Jewels of Gwahlur. Tell

trust to think that someone will do what is right and good

thicket a group of small trees that are very near together

lotus a plant with large, beautiful flowers that smell very nice

Gorulga to send both of them away from Keshan with empty hands. Also, tell Gorulga to give the jewels to Conan the Barbarian – because the gods love him. Can you do that?'

'Sure,' said Muriela.

'Good. Now, wait here!' Conan told her. 'I'll be back soon.'

'Hey, I'm coming with you!' cried Muriela.

'No, you're not. Trust me. You'll be **safe** here,' said Conan.

The barbarian left the oracle room with his sword in his hand. Like a great cat, he moved quickly through the silent palace, and out into the gardens. The evening sky was beginning to darken.

Conan crossed the old road, and moved quietly into the lotus

thicket. The large, flat leaves made a dark green ceiling over his head. At first, the barbarian could see nothing between the trees – only large, white flowers hanging down from their **branches**.

Where was Zargeba hiding?

Just then, Conan saw that one of these flowers had Zargeba's face on it! And Zargeba was looking his way! The barbarian stood as still as stone. 'Has my old enemy seen me coming?' he thought uncomfortably. But Zargeba's head didn't move. Then Conan saw that there was something very strange about that head. 'It's too high above the thicket floor! Zargeba's a short man,' he said to himself. 'Is he standing on something? But where's his body? I can't see anything below his head. It's too dark.'

He moved nearer, and soon understood the mystery: Zargeba's head was hanging by its long black hair from a lotus tree branch. The neck finished in a terrible cut that went right through it. There was no body under that neck, or lying below it on the thicket floor.

Conan looked quickly around him. 'Who **attacked** and killed Zargeba?' he asked himself. 'Was it the priests from Keshan? But where are they now? Or was it someone different?'

Then he thought of Bît-Yakin.

'The old wizard died a long time ago. But what about his servants? Did they ever leave Alkmeenon? Maybe they're still here, and by magic, are still alive.'

Suddenly he remembered Muriela, alone in the oracle room.

'Gods above us!' he thought, hurrying from the thicket.

Just then, he saw a group of men in priestly clothes climbing the stairs to the palace **entrance**. They held burning yellow **torches** high above them.

'The priests from Keshan!' the barbarian said softly.

The High Priest reached the palace entrance first, Conan saw. Ten thin, young priests followed. A tall, strong man came last. Conan knew him at once. It was Tutmekri's secret ally – the traitor priest, Gwarunga!

attack to start fighting; when you start fighting

entrance the way in

torch (plural **torches**) a small fire on the end of a big stick; you carry this with you to give light

23

READING CHECK

Match the first and second parts of these sentences.

a Muriela explains what

b Muriela tells Conan that

c Conan asks Muriela where

d Conan says that he'll help Muriela

e Conan goes outside to find

f Conan sees Zargeba's head which

g The priests from Keshan

1 Gwarunga is a traitor, not Gorulga.

2 Zargeba is, and she tells him.

3 Zargeba told her to say to the High Priest.

4 and kill Zargeba for Muriela.

5 if she speaks to Gorulga for him.

6 arrive, and go into the palace.

7 is hanging by its hair from a tree branch.

WORD WORK

1 Find new words from Chapter 4 in the flowers.

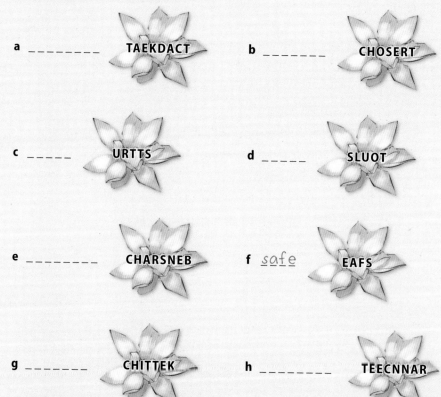

a _ _ _ _ _ _ _ _ TAEKDACT

b _ _ _ _ _ _ _ CHOSERT

c _ _ _ _ _ URTTS

d _ _ _ _ _ SLUOT

e _ _ _ _ _ _ _ _ CHARSNEB

f <u>safe</u> EAFS

g _ _ _ _ _ _ _ CHITTEK

h _ _ _ _ _ _ _ _ TEECNNAR

2 Complete the sentences with the words in Activity 1.

a Conan thinks that Muriela will be ......_safe_...... in the oracle room.

b White stone stairs go up to the front .... of the palace.

c There is a small .... of trees just by the road.

d The beautiful .... flowers smell wonderful.

e Something strange is hanging from one of the tree ....

f Who or what .... Zargeba and killed him?

g When the priests arrive, they are carrying .... because it's dark.

h Conan does not .... Gwarunga because he is a friend of Tutmekri's.

GUESS WHAT

What do you think happens in the next chapter? Complete each sentence with a name.

Conan Gorulga Gwarunga Muriela Yelaya

a .... questions the oracle.

b .... speaks for Conan and against Tutmekri.

c .... tries to kill Muriela.

d .... attacks Gwarunga.

e .... comes back.

CHAPTER FIVE

Enemy Attacks

The priests from Keshan – in fine **furs**, and with long, white **feathers** on their heads – went into the palace. It was a dark, cloudy night now, but their torches were bright. Conan, hiding in the **shadows**, followed. The priests walked down the corridor to the throne room. They crossed the room, and climbed up on the dais. Conan went after them silently.

The priests stood by the gold door. Gorulga **chanted** something. Then all the priests **bowed**, and the feathers on their heads shook. After this, they went into the oracle room, and closed the door.

Conan hurried down the corridor behind the throne. He opened the secret door in the alcove. He could see through the little holes in the wall into the oracle room. He could hear what was happening there, too.

fur something to wear that is made from the skin of an animal; the hair on an animal's body

feather this comes from a bird

shadow a dark shape where there is no light

chant to say words with music in your voice; when you say words with music in your voice

bow to put down your head in front of someone important

Muriela sat like a **statue** on the ivory bed, her back against the wall. The priests stood in front of her, Gorulga in the middle. Once again, his deep voice began chanting. He went on with this for some time. At last, the strange chant finished. The younger priests shouted a short reply.

Then Gorulga moved nearer to Muriela, and said: 'Great Yelaya, we are your priests. We are your slaves. We see only shadows, but you see what will come tomorrow, next month, next year. You speak for the gods. Tell us what we must do: agree to Tutmekri's plan or not?'

Muriela sat up. Conan saw the surprise on the priests' faces.

Then Muriela spoke as the oracle, her voice deep and slow: 'Priests of Alkmeenon, I speak for the gods. I see what you cannot. And I tell you this: Tutmekri and his friend Zargeba are traitors. They want to steal the Jewels of Gwahlur. You must send them from Keshan with empty hands. You must give the jewels to Conan the Barbarian. The gods love him. Under Conan, the army of Keshan will win their fight against the soldiers of Punt.'

In the torch-light, Gorulga's eyes were wild and bright. 'Yelaya has spoken!' he cried. 'When the world began, the gods of light knew that these jewels held the darkest magic. So they told the priests of Alkmeenon to hide them in this valley. Now the gods tell us to bring these jewels from their hiding place. We must give them to Conan the Barbarian. Great Oracle, can we go for them now?'

'Yes. Now go!' replied Muriela, her voice shaking.

'She's afraid. But she did a great job!' Conan thought.

The priests bowed many times and left the room. When they closed the door after them, Muriela fell back against the wall.

'Conan!' she called softly.

statue a picture of a person made of metal or stone

27

'Shhh!' the barbarian replied through the holes in the wall. 'Muriela, it's me! Wait there. I'll come to you.'

He closed the secret door in the alcove. Then he went along the corridor to the throne room. He saw the priests leaving, with their torches, through the far doors. The rest of the throne room was now full of silvery light. Conan looked up through the windows in the ceiling. The clouds hiding the moon earlier were not there now. And the white stones of the palace were now all bright silver.

Just then, Conan heard sounds in the corridor behind him. Were those soft feet on the stone floor? He went to see. Then he heard a woman's scream from the throne room. He pulled his sword from his belt, and hurried back into the great hall.

Muriela stood by the throne. The tall priest Gwarunga was with her. He had one of his strong hands around her neck. Muriela's face was purple.

'Dancing-girl,' cried Gwarunga in a terrible voice, 'are you playing with me? Didn't Zargeba tell you what to say? Didn't you know about Tutmekri's plan? You false slave, I'll kill you for this! But wait... maybe you're just doing what Zargeba wants. I never trusted him! Maybe he's the traitor.'

Looking past Gwarunga's face, Muriela saw Conan coming silently nearer behind the priest. Her eyes brightened – and Gwarunga understood! Suddenly, Conan brought his sword down. At the same time, Gwarunga jumped away. Conan's sword hit the side of the priest's head. Gwarunga dropped to the floor. He was **unconscious**, but not dead.

'Gwarunga came back,' cried Muriela, now free. 'He attacked me in the oracle room, and pulled me here. I thought that he was going to kill me. Let's leave Alkmeenon.'

'After we find the Jewels of Gwahlur,' said Conan. He looked at Muriela. 'Poor you! There's a hole in your dress, and in the attack you lost that big jewel from your hair.'

'I'll get it from the oracle room,' said Muriela. 'After that, we'll stay together!'

While Muriela went for the jewel, Conan turned to Gwarunga. The traitor-priest still lay unconscious on the ground. Conan needed to finish the job, and kill him. He pulled Gwarunga into the corridor to do this. But just when he had his sword at the priest's neck, he heard Muriela's cry.

'Conan! She's back!'

Suddenly there was a scream, and the sound of soft feet on the stone floor. After that, everything was silent.

Conan ran into the oracle room. He saw the beautiful woman in her dress and jewels on the ivory bed. 'Muriela, what are you doing?' he cried. But when he touched her, she was cold. This was not Muriela. It was Yelaya!

Then Conan saw: there was no hole in her dress, and all her jewels were in place.

'Someone dressed Yelaya in new clothes and brought her back!' he cried. 'That same person also took Muriela. But who, and how?'

unconscious
sleeping because you are ill or someone hit you

29

READING CHECK

Correct nine more mistakes in the story.

Conan

~~Jutmekri~~ follows the priests down the corridor to the throne room. The priests go into the oracle room and close the cupboard behind them. Conan goes to the alcove behind the throne. He watches and listens through the holes in the wall. Gorulga questions the oracle about giving the throne of Gwahlur to Jutmekri. Muriela tells the High Priest what Zargeba asked her to say: to give the jewels to him, and to send Jutmekri and Conan away from Keshan with nothing. Gorulga and the young priests leave to find the jewels. Gwarunga stays behind and attacks Yelaya, trying to kill her. Conan finds the two of them together, standing by the bed. He hits Gwarunga on the head with his sword and knocks him to the floor. Muriela goes to find the flower which fell from her head in the oracle room. Conan is just going to kill Gwarunga, but then he hears Muriela's laugh from the oracle room. He leaves Gwarunga and goes to see what has happened. In the oracle room he finds that Muriela has gone, and that Yelaya is on the throne.

WORD WORK

Correct the underlined word in each sentence.

a The priests are wearing <u>flowers</u> on their heads. ..feathers..

b They are also wearing animal <u>fires</u> because it's a cold night. ....

c Conan stays in the <u>shakers</u> because he doesn't want anybody to see him. ....

d Gorulga and the other priests <u>change</u> strange words together. ....

e All the priests <u>show</u> their heads many times, too. ....

f After Conan hits Gwarunga, the traitor priest lies <u>uncomfortable</u> on the floor. ....

GUESS WHAT

What do you think happens in the next chapter? Tick four boxes.

Conan…

a ☐ finds a secret door in the oracle room wall.

b ☐ sees some interesting pictures on a wall.

c ☐ soon finds Muriela alive.

d ☐ escapes just in time from a big stone that falls on him.

e ☐ kills Gwarunga while he is still unconscious.

f ☐ follows the priests across the valley.

g ☐ meets Bît-Yakin's servants in a cave.

h ☐ listens to a conversation between Gorulga and Bît-Yakin.

CHAPTER SIX
Where is Muriela?

'Muriela! Where are you?' called Conan.

He looked around the oracle room for a secret door, and at last he found it. In one of the white stone walls, there was a long, thin crack, as tall as a man. In this crack, Conan could see a small piece of fine, white **cloth** from Muriela's dress.

'So they took her through here, and the closing door caught part of her dress in the doorway!' thought Conan.

He put his knife to the crack, and opened the secret door. Inside, he saw stairs going down. He put his knife against the bottom of the open door and pushed it down into a crack between the stones in the floor, to stop the door from closing behind him.

After that, he went through the door and down the stairs. At the bottom, he saw a number of pictures on the wall, by a dark, narrow corridor entrance. The pictures showed the city of Alkmeenon many years before. Conan stopped for a second and looked at them. There was Yelaya on her ivory bed in the oracle room. Priests were standing by her, and a little old man in yellow was standing by the alcove, his mouth near the holes in the wall.

'The wizard Bît-Yakin!' cried Conan. 'He's speaking for the oracle, and working for her, too!' Other pictures showed the old man bringing new clothes for Yelaya to wear.

cloth clothes are made of this

'And what about his servants?' Conan thought. Then he saw them. Strange, tall **figures** walked through the empty palace. The short figure of Bît-Yakin spoke to them, pointing here and there, giving them different jobs. These same tall figures hung from ladders over a river far under the ground, pulling dark things out of the water.

Conan remembered the scroll that came from the mummy's cave. At last he understood. The mystery of Bît-Yakin and his servants was a mystery no more.

He turned to the narrow corridor, and began to walk down it.

'Hmm, there's that strange animal smell again!' He remembered it well from the courtyard of the gong.

Far along the dark corridor before him, he heard noises. Maybe it was the sound of feet on the stone floor. Maybe it was the cloth of a dress moving against the narrow stone walls. He hurried after these sounds, holding his hands before his face.

Minutes later, Conan's hands touched a metal door. It closed the corridor before him. He pushed it, but could not move it.

Just then, he heard the sound of someone pulling a **lever** on the other side of the door. Conan jumped back, and just in time. A large and heavy square stone dropped from the ceiling of the tunnel. It landed noisily on the floor by the door – where Conan was standing seconds before.

'Gods help us!' cried the barbarian.

Muriela was on the other side of the metal door, he was sure. But now he could not move the stone or open the door.

'I must go back and find another way!' he cried.

He hurried back to the stairs. But just when he started climbing them, the door at the top closed. He pushed against this door, but could not move it. Then his hands found a **bolt**.

'Maybe that fell into place by accident when the door closed,' he thought.

figure someone that you can't see very well

lever a long stick that you move to make something work

bolt a piece of wood or metal that you put across a door to stop someone opening it

He pulled back the bolt, and pushed against the door once more. This time it opened. Conan walked back into the oracle room, and looked around him.

His knife was not in the crack in the floor any more. The ivory bed of the oracle was also empty. Was Yelaya really alive after all? Then he saw blood on the floor. He followed the blood back to the corridor behind the throne, but that was empty, too.

'Right. So maybe Gwarunga woke up and came after me,' thought Conan. 'He saw my knife in the floor by the door and pulled it out. Then he closed the door just before I could reach it. But that still doesn't explain about Yelaya!'

Conan wanted to find Muriela, but he didn't know where to begin. 'What can I do?' he thought. Then it came to him, like a voice in his head: 'Follow the priests. Find the Jewels of Gwahlur. Maybe you can learn where Muriela is on the way to their hiding place.'

He hurried from the palace to the gardens. For a man from the north, following people was easy: here were **tracks** on the ground, there someone pushed a tree branch earlier and broke it.

Conan moved quickly across the dark valley, following the priests' tracks. He walked through thickets, and past large flowers that hung from strange plants and smelt very sweet. Soon he could see the priests' torches and tall, white head-feathers in front of him. The priests were bowing and chanting, and moving very slowly.

'That's lucky,' thought Conan.

When at last he came near the priests, they were beside the cliff wall – the part nearest to the palace. There were strange statues in alcoves in the stone wall here: statues of men, gods, and figures that were half-man and half-animal. They were older than the palace of Alkmeenon and everything in it.

tracks people or animals moving across a place leave these on the ground behind them; people coming after can use these to follow a person or animal

'I'm going away from the place where I left Muriela,' Conan said to himself. 'But I'm sure that there are many old tunnels under the ground here. And those tunnels go from the palace to all parts of this valley! Maybe I'll find her soon.'

When Gorulga and his priests went through a doorway in the cliff wall, Conan went after them. The doorway was like a large **monster's** mouth in the side of the cliff. The metal door stood open. It had many bolts on it. Conan stopped by the open door for a second or two.

'Do I go in or wait outside?' he asked himself. He didn't want the priests to bolt the door and leave him outside, so he decided to go in. He needed to find the Jewels of Gwahlur! He didn't worry about how he would get out later.

Walking after the priests down a long tunnel, Conan saw that its walls were bright with **phosphorescence**. This helped him to see where he was going.

At the end of this tunnel, Conan found himself in a small, round cave with seven tunnel mouths in the far wall. In front of the middle tunnel stood a statue of an ugly animal-god. Conan could see torches in the tunnel behind the statue. He quickly went after them.

monster a big animal that is very bad to look at, and makes people afraid

phosphorescence a soft light that comes naturally from things like cave walls, or small sea animals

At the end of this second tunnel, Conan found himself in a larger cave. There was a bigger and uglier statue here. Gorulga and his priests stood in front of this. They held their torches high, and were bowing and chanting to the statue. When they finished, they walked down the tunnel behind it. Conan went after them.

At the end of the third tunnel, Conan found an even bigger cave. There was a really ugly animal-god statue here. In front of this, Gorulga and the priests were on their **knees**. With their torches still in their hands, they bowed and chanted.

Conan hid in the shadows, and watched. 'Hmm, Gwarunga's not with them. But I don't think that they've seen that,' he thought.

The barbarian looked round the great cave. A number of large circular ledges went around it, one above the other, nearly reaching the stone ceiling. Conan noted the narrow stone stairs that went up to these ledges from the cave floor.

The priests were still chanting and bowing busily, when suddenly there was a great cry from high up in the cave. Gorulga and his followers stopped chanting at once and looked up, afraid. Conan also turned his eyes to the dark ceiling. There, on the highest ledge, a smoky blue light burned in the shadows. It lit a small figure in a fine white dress, with jewels in her hair.

'Yelaya, why have you followed us?' screamed Gorulga. 'What do you want?'

From the high ledge, the reply came back. The large, empty cave made the voice strangely loud, and difficult to **recognize**.

'Do you think that the oracle is not true? Do you think that the gods are not real? False people of Keshan, you will be sorry for what you did!'

READING CHECK

Are these sentences true or false? Tick the boxes.

		True	False
a	Conan finds a piece of Muriela's shoe in a crack in the wall.	☐	☑
b	Conan uses his sword to open a secret door in the wall.	☐	☐
c	Conan goes down some secret stairs and sees some wall pictures.	☐	☐
d	The old pictures show Bît-Yakin and his servants in Alkmeenon.	☐	☐
e	Conan goes down a bright corridor until a metal door stops him.	☐	☐
f	A heavy circular stone falls down suddenly and nearly kills him.	☐	☐
g	Conan goes back to the secret door, but someone has broken it.	☐	☐
h	Conan pushes the door open, and goes back into the oracle room.	☐	☐
i	Yelaya has gone, and the corridor behind the throne is empty.	☐	☐
j	Conan follows Gorulga and his priests across the palace gardens.	☐	☐
k	They go through a door in the ground and into some caves.	☐	☐
l	Conan hears an angry voice coming from the top of one cave.	☐	☐

WORD WORK

Use the words in the knife to complete what Conan is thinking on page 39.

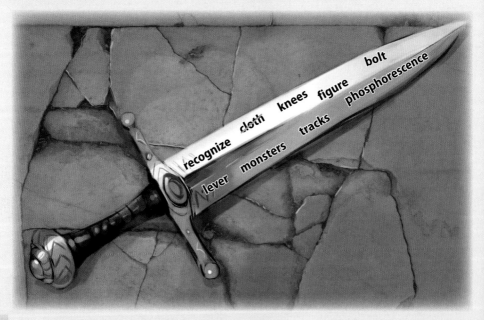

recognize · cloth · knees · figure · bolt · lever · monsters · tracks · phosphorescence

Hey, there's some white **a)** .....cloth..... . It's from Muriela's dress. There's a secret door in the wall!

Hmm, these old wall pictures are so interesting. That **b)** .... in yellow clothes is the old wizard, Bît-Yakin. And those tall, gray **c)** .... are his servants.

Uh-oh! I just heard someone pulling a **d)** .... on the other side of this metal door. Dangerous! I must get out of here – fast.

Oh, no! Someone's closed the secret door. I can't see anything. But wait. I can feel a **e)** .... here. Maybe if I pull it back, the door will open. Yes-s-s!

Aha! I can see **f)** .... on the ground. Let's have a look. Yes, I **g)** .... them: priestly shoes. Gorulga and the others came this way.

What's that strange light in here? Oh, now I see! It's **h)** .... coming from the cave walls.

Look at that! The priests are all down on their **i)** .... in front of that strange statue.

GUESS WHAT

What do you think happens in the next chapter? Complete the sentences with the names. You can use some names more than once.

Conan Gorulga Gwarunga Muriela Yelaya

a .... thinks that .... is speaking to him.

b .... and his followers go to find the Jewels of Gwahlur.

c .... dies fighting after he attacks and tries to kill ....

d .... is a prisoner in a small cave, but .... helps her to escape.

CHAPTER SEVEN

The Servants of Bît-Yakin

'But, Yelaya,' Gorulga cried. 'In the oracle room, you told us to find the Jewels of Gwahlur, and give them to Conan.'

'Do not **believe** what you heard there,' replied the voice. 'That was a false oracle. I am truly Yelaya, and I say: bring the jewels to Keshan. Give them to Tutmekri. He will take them to the temple in Zembabwei. They will be safe there. Then find Conan the Barbarian, and kill him. The gods have spoken!'

Gorulga and his priests stood up. They hurried down the corridor behind the statue. At the same time, Conan climbed the stone stairs to the highest ledge in the cave. He wanted to understand: was Muriela a traitor? Or was this really Yelaya?

When he reached the ledge, he found the answer. The cold, dead body of Yelaya stood against a **pillar** of stone.

Just then, something jumped from the dark tunnel behind Conan. The barbarian heard, pulled his sword from his belt, and

believe to feel sure that something is true

pillar a tall thing that sometimes has a statue or the top of a building on it

turned fast. The attacker's knife missed Conan's back. But the barbarian's sword went right through his enemy's body. Conan pulled his sword out, and the man fell back on the ledge. It was Gwarunga, and he was dead.

Conan went back to look at Yelaya's body. There were **ropes** around her knees and her middle. These held her body up against the pillar. Long ropes of her strong hair went back around the pillar, too. So her head stayed up. From the cave floor, in the blue and smoky light, you could not see the ropes. So you could easily believe that she was standing there, alive.

Turning back to Gwarunga's body, Conan put the pieces of his enemy's story together. 'So, you woke up in the corridor behind the throne, and went into the oracle room. You recognized my knife in the floor, and knew that I was down the secret stairs. So you pulled out my knife, and closed the door before I came back.'

Conan took his knife from Gwarunga's fingers. He put it back in his belt. Then he went on: 'Next, you carried Yelaya's dead body through a secret tunnel under the palace gardens. You knew that Gorulga and his priests would come this way. So you hurried to this cave. You **tied** Yelaya's body against that pillar. Then you waited. When the priests arrived, you used magic blue "temple fire" to light the body. Maybe Tutmekri gave you this. You spoke the oracle's words yourself. You knew that it wouldn't be easy to recognize one voice from another in this large cave.'

Just then, the blue fire stopped burning. But Conan could still see. Phosphorescence came from another tunnel that opened onto the ledge where he was standing. He went over to this tunnel and walked down it. He could hear the chanting priests in front of him. Maybe this corridor went down to a ledge in the large cave that the priests wanted to reach. A short way down the tunnel, Conan saw a doorway on his left. He decided to go through it.

rope a very thick, strong string

tie to keep something in place with rope

He found himself in a small cave with bright phosphorescence on its walls. In the middle of the cave, there was a big metal statue of a monster-god. A white figure was lying across the statue's metal knees. Gold **chains** tied her to the statue to stop her escaping. It was Muriela.

'Conan!' she cried. 'You found me!'

Conan quickly cut the chains with his sword. 'You're free now, Muriela. But what happened?'

Muriela told her story:

When I went into the oracle room to find the jewel from my hair, I saw Yelaya on her bed. I shouted to you. But then many strong hands caught me from behind. Something put its hand over my mouth, and

chain a long string of metal that is very strong

pulled me through a secret door in the wall. We went down some stairs, and along a dark corridor. We went past some metal doors, and into a lighter cave. Then I saw them.

My attackers were monsters! They had arms and legs. They walked like men. But they were very tall and strong, with gray fur all over them. They spoke in strange animal cries. They closed the metal doors behind them, and waited. Soon someone tried to open the doors from the other side. One of the monsters pulled a lever in the wall, and something heavy crashed down behind the doors.

After that, those gray monsters left the cave with the lever in. They carried me through many different tunnels, and brought me upstairs to this cave. They chained me to this statue, and then left me here.

Finishing her story, Muriela turned to Conan. 'Those gray monster-men – what are they?' she cried.

'The servants of Bît-Yakin,' answered Conan. He was putting together the story of Alkeemon. He knew some things from his time in Keshan, and he now had more information from the mummy's letter, and the pictures on the wall of Bît-Yakin and his servants. He told this story to Muriela.

A long time ago, the wizard Bît-Yakin came to Alkmeenon from the city of Asgalun. He spoke for the oracle when priests came from Keshan to ask her questions. He worked for Yelaya, and changed her clothes when this was necessary. He used magic on her body to stop it from **becoming** old. Nobody knew that Bît-Yakin and his servants lived in Alkmeenon. They always hid themselves from visitors.

Bît-Yakin stopped himself from becoming old by magic. He also used strong magic on his strange servants. Because of this, they did everything that he told them.

The old wizard ate the food that the priests brought for the gods. His servants ate dead bodies that they pulled from the river below the city.

become (*past* **became**, **become**) to begin to be

This river comes from the country of Punt. The priests in Punt put their dead people in this river. So Bît-Yakin's servants built ladders over the water and hung from these to catch their food.

Then, after hundreds of years, Bît-Yakin died. His servants left his body in a cave in the cliffs. But the servants stayed in Alkmeenon.

The next time that priests visited the oracle, Bît-Yakin's servants attacked and killed the High Priest. The old wizard was dead, and nobody could stop them.

After that, no one from Keshan visited Yelaya for hundreds of years. Not until Gorulga came to ask her about Tutmekri's plan.

Conan went on: 'Bît-Yakin's servants dressed Yelaya and brought her back after Zargeba took her. They knew how to do this because they watched the wizard do the same when he was alive. Somewhere in the palace there's a secret room full of fine clothes for the oracle, I'm sure. Those gray monsters also killed Zargeba, and hung his head from a tree.'

'Oh, so I won't have any more trouble from him!' said Muriela, her face brightening.

'No,' agreed Conan. 'But let's go after the priests. Before I killed him, Gwarunga told Gorulga that your words in the oracle room were false. So stealing the Jewels of Gwahlur is the only way that I can have them now.'

'And what about the servants of Bît-Yakin?' asked Muriela.

'Well, they've hidden from us, and they haven't attacked openly. Who knows what they're thinking? Let's worry about them later,' replied the barbarian.

'All right!' cried Muriela. 'But this time you're not leaving me behind!'

Conan and Muriela walked down the tunnel together. At the end of the tunnel, they reached a **huge** cave. They were standing on a ledge near the top. There was another ledge on the

huge very big

44

same side of the cave below them.

Across the floor of the cave, running from one side to the other, flowed a fast moving river. A narrow stone bridge went across the river from the ledge where Conan and Muriela stood to the other side of the cave. Just under this, a second bridge crossed the cave from the ledge below to a ledge on the far cave wall. Stone stairs came up from the cave floor to the near end of the bottom bridge, and stairs went from both ends of the higher bridge to the bridge under it.

The strong phosphorescence from the stone walls lit the huge cave well. But, at the other end of the higher bridge, Conan could see a different light. Through a doorway in the cave wall, he could see stars in the night sky. Maybe they could escape from Alkmeenon that way?

READING CHECK

Write an answer from the box for each question.

> a river   Bît-Yakin's servants   Conan   dead bodies   ~~Gwarunga~~   Bît-Yakin's servants
> stone bridges   the Jewels of Gwahlur   the night sky   Bît-Yakin's servants
> Muriela   Gwarunga   Bît-Yakin's servants

a Who speaks to Gorulga as the Oracle Yelaya? .Gwarunga.

b What must Gorulga give to Tutmekri later? ....

c Who must Gorulga kill later? ....

d Who does Conan kill in a fight? ....

e Who does Conan find as a prisoner in a small cave? ....

f Who killed Zargeba and hung his head on a tree? ....

g Who brought Yelaya back to the oracle room? ....

h Who took Muriela from the oracle room? ....

i Who tried to kill Conan in the tunnel? ....

j What do Bît-Yakin's servants eat? ....

k What crosses the floor of the huge cave that Conan and Muriela find? ....

l What two things cross the cave above this? ....

m What can Conan see through a doorway at the end of the higher of these? ....

WORD WORK

1 Find six more new words from Chapter 7 in the letter square.

D	I	J	O	R	I	M	A	S
U	M	R	O	P	E	G	D	S
O	T	X	D	I	E	G	J	H
M	C	I	I	L	A	N	A	L
H	B	B	E	L	I	E	V	E
A	V	U	M	A	H	R	U	K
M	X	K	H	R	G	U	R	L
B	E	C	O	M	E	T	G	Q
X	C	P	L	D	E	M	H	E

2 Complete each sentences with the correct form of a word in Activity 1.

a Gwarunga ......tied...... Yelaya's body in place before the others arrived.

b A number of .... stopped her body from falling.

c Through blue smoke, the priests saw Yelaya standing in front of a stone ....

d Gorulga .... that the voice which he heard was Yelaya's.

e Muriela was a prisoner with .... on her arms and legs when Conan found her.

f When Conan arrived, Muriela .... happy once more.

g Conan and Muriel reached a .... cave with a river in it.

GUESS WHAT

What do you think happens in the last chapter?
Tick two boxes to finish each sentence.

a Bît-Yakin's servants…

   1 ☐ try to hide the Jewels of Gwahlur.

   2 ☐ kill Gorulga and his followers.

   3 ☐ try to catch Conan and Muriela.

b Conan…

   1 ☐ takes the Jewels of Gwahlur.

   2 ☐ leaves the Jewels of Gwahlur with Muriela.

   3 ☐ kills many of Bît-Yakin's servants.

c Muriela…

   1 ☐ becomes a prisoner of one of Bît-Yakin's servants.

   2 ☐ drops the Jewels of Gwahlur in the river.

   3 ☐ falls from one of the bridges.

CHAPTER EIGHT
A Difficult Choice

Conan looked down from the high ledge where he and Muriela stood. What were Gorulga and his priests doing?

The High Priest and his followers stood in a corner of the huge cave, on the near side of the river. They put their torches into a half-circle of holes in the ground in front of a stone **altar**. This had a square top, and there was no statue on it. Behind the altar, the walls of the huge cave were dark.

While Conan and Muriela watched, the priests chanted and bowed. Gorulga **lifted** his arms. Moving nearer to the altar, he put a hand on the square top, and lifted it up. From inside, the High Priest pulled out a small, metal box. Then he closed the altar, put the metal box on top, and opened it.

From the ledge high above, Conan and Muriela saw the wonderful, magic blue light that flowed from the jewels. It was like living fire!

'The Jewels of Gwahlur!' cried the barbarian. 'At last!'

The torches were nothing, the phosphorescence was nothing, next to those bright jewels! The cave walls became darker. In the corner behind the altar, they were now black.

'When the world began, the gods took these jewels from their greatest enemy, the dark king, Gwahlur,' cried Gorulga. 'The jewels held Gwahlur's magic. Without them, he was **weak**. The priests of Alkmeenon hid them in this altar. Now we must take them to Tutmekri for the good of Keshan and our new ally Zembabwei!'

Just then, Conan and Muriela saw something new. Around the dark doorway behind the altar, there were strange figures on the cave wall – like huge, gray statues. They had arms and legs like men, but gray fur like **apes**. And their cold, blue eyes were alive!

altar a special, high table in a temple or a church

lift to move up

weak not strong

ape a group of animals; chimpanzees and gorillas are apes

Gorulga screamed when he saw them. He fell back, afraid.
Then he tried to take the box of jewels from the altar.

The nearest of the ape-men put out a long arm and caught
the High Priest by the neck. It threw him down on the altar, and
broke his head like an egg.

The priests pulled knives and swords from their belts, but these
did not help them. The servants of Bît-Yakin were strong and
fast. They killed the young priests one after the other, in terrible
ways. Soon nearly all the priests were dead. Only one young
man still lived. He ran, screaming, up the tunnel to the higher
caves, and all the gray ape-men hurried after him.

'Muriela,' cried Conan, 'I must have those jewels!'

'No!' replied the slave-girl.

'Yes!' said Conan. 'Wait here. I won't be long!'

The barbarian didn't use the stone stairs. It was quicker to jump down from ledge to ledge. Soon he reached the altar. He pushed Gorulga's dead body to one side, and took the jewel box in his hands. He looked at the dark, strangely beautiful stones. Then he closed the box, and put it under his arm. He began climbing the stone stairs. He did not want to fight the servants of Bît-Yakin. They were cold killers. He knew that now.

At last, Conan reached the ledge where Muriela was waiting. 'Let's go,' he said. He took her to the narrow stone bridge, and they began to cross. When they were in the middle, Muriela looked down. She saw the fast-moving river far below. She saw the **wide** bridge just under the narrow bridge that they were on. Suddenly, she felt afraid.

wide not narrow

'I c-c-can't go on!' she cried.

'You must!' answered Conan. 'Don't look down. Look across the bridge.'

'But it's so narrow!'

'Look at the stars through the tunnel in front of us!'

He pointed with his free hand at the tunnel entrance on the far side. Muriela began walking across the bridge again, and Conan followed her.

When they were through the tunnel, they found themselves on a high ledge on the outside of Alkmeenon's cliff wall. Conan looked down.

'It won't be easy for Muriela,' he thought. 'But I believe that we can get down there fast. Then we can escape through the jungle.' He began to take off his belt. He wanted to tie the jewel box to his back.

Just then, he heard a noise from the tunnel behind them.

'Wait here!' he told Muriela, leaving her with the jewels. His sword in his hand, he walked back through the tunnel into the cave. Inside, a gray ape-man was crossing the narrow stone bridge over the river. 'It's following our tracks,' cried Conan. 'But it's alone. I must kill it before the others come back.'

He ran to meet the monster in the middle of the high bridge. Quickly he put his sword deep into the figure's gray side. The ape-man was hurt, and angry. It hit Conan with one of its long gray arms, and he fell off the top bridge. Luckily the barbarian caught the side of the bridge below with his hand while he was falling. He pulled himself up onto the lower bridge, and waited to see what the monster would do next.

The ape-man looked down angrily at Conan. It was losing blood from the deep sword-cut in its side. It moved weakly across to the stairs between the bridge that it was on and the bridge where Conan stood. Then it stopped and looked at the tunnel entrance in the cave wall on that side.

Conan looked, too, to see what was more interesting for the monster than him. Muriela stood in the tunnel entrance, the metal jewel box under her arm.

Quickly the monster caught Muriela. It put her under one arm, and the jewel box under the other arm. Then it began to come back across the higher bridge. It was moving slowly now. It had lost a lot of blood from the cut in its side, and it was becoming weak. When it reached the middle, its eyes closed, and it fell off the bridge unconscious, dropping what it held.

choice when
you decide which
of different things
you want

save to take
someone or
something out of
danger

The ape-man hit the side of the bridge below, and dropped
down into the river. Muriela fell to one side of the bridge, and
held onto it with one hand. The jewel box fell on the other
side, hit the bridge, and began falling again. This made a
difficult **choice** for Conan: the jewels, or Muriela? He could
not **save** both.

But really it was no choice. Conan moved over to Muriela, caught her hand in his, and pulled her up. The box of wonderful jewels fell into the fast moving river below, which carried it quickly away from the world of men.

Lifting Muriela in his arms, Conan climbed the stairs to the higher ledge. Suddenly, he heard angry cries from below. The other servants of Bît-Yakin were back. Their long teeth and hands were red with blood. They saw Conan and Muriela above them, and they began coming up the stone stairs to catch them.

Conan and Muriela hurried along the tunnel to the outside of the cliff wall. They climbed down the cliff as fast as they could. When the angry gray faces looked over the ledge, they saw Conan and Muriela far below. They were at the foot of the cliff, escaping into the jungle.

'I don't believe that those monsters will come after us outside the valley,' said Conan. 'We're safe now!'

'Oh, Conan! I am sorry!' cried Muriela.

'What for?' asked the barbarian.

'You lost the jewels! Why did you save me and not them?'

'Forget it. It's no good worrying over past choices, is it?' said Conan. 'Let's go to Punt. I'll tell the people there that Zembabwei and Keshan are making plans to attack them. Maybe I can teach the soldiers of Punt how to win against their attackers. All for money, of course!' he laughed.

'I believe that the people of Punt have a great temple in their city with a beautiful ivory oracle in it,' said Muriela happily. 'If I can change places with her, we'll surely walk away with a lot of gold, and expensive jewels!'

Smiling, the two of them walked happily together into the night.

READING CHECK

Correct the mistakes in the sentences.

a The priests' torches are standing in a half-~~square~~. *circle*

b Gorulga takes the Jewels of Gwahlur from behind the altar.

c The jewels once belonged to the bright king, Gwahlur.

d Bît-Yakin's servants start helping the priests.

e The last priest to die is the High Priest, Gorulga.

f The ape-men follow one old priest to the higher caves.

g Conan climbs down some stone stairs to steal the jewels.

h Conan helps Muriela across the narrow wood bridge.

i Conan leaves Muriela without the jewels on a high cliff ledge.

j Conan hurts the ape-man, then drops to the river below.

k The ape-man flies, dropping Muriela and the jewels.

l Conan catches Muriela, and together they leave for Keshan.

WORD WORK

Use new words from Chapter 8 to correct the boxed words in these sentences.

a A square stone `answer` .... stands in one corner of the cave.

b The second bridge isn't narrow, it's `wild` ..... *wide* ....

c Can you `live` .... that box, or is it too heavy for you?

d Bît-Yakin's servants are like big, gray `apples` ....

e After losing a lot of blood, the strong monster becomes `well` ....

f Conan `sails` .... Muriela from a dangerous fall into the river.

g Conan can do one thing only. He has no `voice` .... in what he does.

GUESS WHAT

What do you think happens after the story ends? Choose from these ideas or add your own.

a ☐ Conan and Muriela make a lot of money in Punt.

b ☐ Punt wins the fight against Keshan and Zembabwei.

c ☐ Conan marries Muriela and they have many children.

d ☐ Conan leaves Muriela to look for gold and jewels again.

e ☐ ....

f ☐ ....

Project A *Famous lost treasures*

1 **Read the text and write notes in the information table below. Use a dictionary to help you.**

King John's treasure belonged to King John 'the bad', Robin Hood's enemy. In October 1216, the king was in the east of England when he became very ill. He decided to travel home around 'the Wash'. This was the name of a marsh near Lincoln. The sea often covered the land here. Because it was the shorter way, King John's soldiers took carts with his jewels in them across the marsh. The sea came in, and the soldiers lost the treasure. King John's treasure contained: a crown, a gold stick with a white bird on it, the great fighter Tristan's sword, gold coins, silver plates and gold cups. It was worth about 40 million pounds in today's money. No one knows where it is now.

Name of treasure?	
Who did it belong to?	
Who lost it?	
Where?	
When?	
What did it contain?	
How much was it worth?	

2 **Read the notes about another lost treasure and complete the text on page 57.**

Name of treasure?	the Kruger millions
Who did it belong to?	the Boers of South Africa
Who lost it?	the President of the Boers, Paul Kruger
Where?	the North-eastern Transvaal (= part of the country between the Vaal and Limpopo rivers)
When?	October 1900
What did it contain?	gold and silver coins, gold and silver bars, gold dust
How much was it worth?	150 million pounds

.... is the name of a South-African lost treasure. In the year ...., Britain was fighting against the .... of .... The .... were afraid because the British were moving nearer to their capital city, Pretoria. So they gave a lot of their treasure to ...., who was their .... He traveled across the .... to Mozambique and left for France in the month of .... But the treasure stayed in Africa. It contained .... coins, bars, and dust, and .... coin and bars. It was worth about .... million pounds in today's money. Nobody has ever found it.

3 **Do you know about any other famous lost treasures? Research and write about one. Use the texts in Activities 1 and 2 to help you.**

The Amber Room

Blackbeard's Silver

Montezuma's Treasure

Yamashita's Gold

Project B *A '5 Ws' poem*

A '5 Ws' poem is a poem of five lines that answers the questions Who? What? Where? When? Why? in that order.

1 The lines of this 5 Ws poem about Yelaya's death are in the wrong order. Write the lines in the correct order in the table below.

a) Because they wanted to say their last goodbyes.

b) Lying on her cold white bed

c) Came to see their only daughter, Princess Yelaya,

d) The King and Queen of Alkmeenon

e) Soon after she died,

Who?	
What?	
Where?	
When?	
Why?	

2 Read this 5 Ws poem about the Jewels of Gwahlur. Match each synonym below with a boxed word in the poem.

The selfless gods of light
Told priests to bury the jewels of the dead Gwahlur
In deep caves beneath Alkmeenon
At the dawn of time
To stop these terrible stones from corrupting the world.

Synonyms

a) beginning – ....

b) making bad – ....

c) put under the ground – ....

d) thinking of others – ....

e) under – ....

3 Complete this 5 Ws poem about the King of Zembabwei with the words in the box. Use a dictionary to help you.

crafty land neighbors tricksters war

The **a)** .... King of Zembabwei

Sent the two **b)** .... Tutmekri and Zargeba

To the **c)** .... of Keshan

Before he attacked his Puntish **d)** ....

To make the Keshanis his allies in a **e)** ....

    that they would lose.

4 Choose a different character from *Conan the Barbarian: The Jewels of Gwahlur* for a 5 Ws poem.

Conan   **Muriela**   **Zargeba**

Tutmekri   **Bît-Yakin**   **Bît-Yakin's servants**

Gorulga

Gwarunga

Make notes for your poem about this character in the 5 Ws graphic organizer.

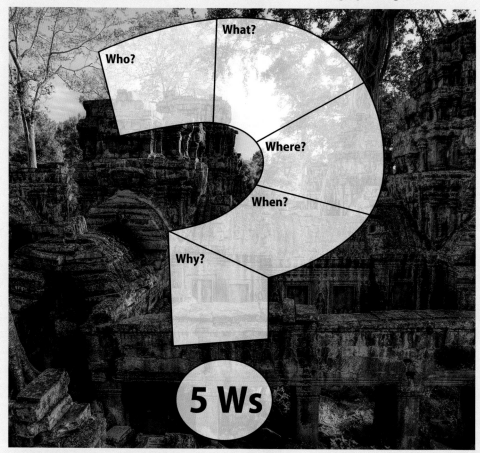

What?
Who?
Where?
When?
Why?

5 Ws

5 Write your 5 Ws poem in the grid below.

Who?	
What?	
Where?	
When?	
Why?	

6 Organize a poetry reading with your classmates. Read your poems aloud. Vote for your favorites.

GRAMMAR

GRAMMAR CHECK

To + infinitive or _-ing_ form verb

After the verbs begin, decide, forget, learn, like, need, remember, try, want, and would like we use to + infinitive.

Conan decides to steal the jewels for himself.

After the verbs begin, enjoy, finish, go, go on, like, love, prefer, remember, and stop we use verb + -ing.

Conan prefers climbing without shoes.

With the verb remember, the meaning changes with to + infinitive or verb + -ing.

Conan remembers to take the letter with him.

(= the remembering is first and looks forward to the taking)

Conan remembers meeting Tutmekri and Zargeba in Keshan.

(= the remembering is second and looks back to the meeting)

With the verbs begin and like, the meaning does not change.

Tutmekri begins to speak / speaking to the king.

Zargeba likes to have / having slaves.

1 **Complete each sentence about the story with the to + infinitive or verb + _-ing_ form of the verb in brackets.**

a Conan wants . .to arrive. . (arrive) in Alkmeenon before Gorulga.

b Conan likes . . . . (teach) the army of Keshan new ways of fighting.

c Conan tries . . . . (find) the Jewels of Gwahlur in Keshan, but he can't.

d Tutmekri enjoys . . . . (make) big plans.

e Conan remembers . . . . (fight) against Tutmekri a long time ago.

f After a while, Conan stops . . . . (listen) to Tutmekri's false words.

g The King of Keshan waits until Tutmekri finishes . . . . (speak).

h Gorulga needs . . . . (ask) Yelaya about Tutmekri's plan.

i Everyone begins . . . . (talk) excitedly about the oracle.

j After Conan leaves, he goes on . . . . (walk) into the jungle.

k Conan learned . . . . (climb) in the cold north when he was a boy.

l He doesn't forget . . . . (put) his sword on his back before he starts.

m He remembers . . . . (take) off his shoes, too.

GRAMMAR CHECK

Past Simple *yes / no* questions and short answers

We use was / were or the auxiliary verbs did and could + infinitive **without to** in yes / no questions in the Past Simple.

Was Muriela a slave?

Did she live in Alkmeenon?

In the short answer, we repeat the subject and re-use was / were or the auxiliary verb.

Yes, she was.

No, she didn't.

2 Write answers for the questions. Use the short answers in the box.

> No, he couldn't.   No, he didn't.   No, he wasn't.   No, they weren't.
> Yes, he could.   Yes, he did.   ~~Yes, he did.~~   Yes, it did.   Yes, there was.

a Did Conan find the gong? .....Yes, he did...

b Did he see a big, gray animal near it? ....

c Did he smell something strange in the courtyard? ....

d Did the old stone floor break under Conan's feet? ....

e Was there a river under the palace? ....

f Was Conan afraid of dying in it? ....

g Could Conan swim well? ....

h Were the ladders in the tunnel new? ....

i Could Conan find the Jewels of Gwahlur easily? ....

3 Write short answers for these questions about Muriela.

a Was she from Punt? .No, she wasn't..

b Could she speak like an oracle? ....

c Was she beautiful? ....

d Could she hide her Corinthian way of speaking? ....

e Did she arrive in Alkmeenon with Zargeba? ....

f Did she climb over the cliff wall? ....

GRAMMAR CHECK

Linkers: *so* and *because*

We use *so* to link two sentences when the second sentence explains a result.

Tutmekri was Conan's enemy so the barbarian didn't believe him.

(= result of first part of sentence)

We use *because* to link two sentences when the second sentence explains a reason.

The traitors visited Keshan because they had a plan.

(= reason for first part of sentence)

4 Match a-i with 1-9. Complete the sentences using *so* or *because*.

a Tutmekri and Zargeba worked together…
because they were friends.

b They met the King of Keshan…
....

c Punt was Keshan's enemy…
....

d Keshan had a weak army…
....

e They spoke for King of Zembabewei…
....

f Gorulga believed in the oracle…
....

g Gwarunga needed money…
....

h They wanted the Jewels of Gwahlur…
....

i They asked for Conan's death…
....

1 they asked for some for Zembabwei.

2 they spoke against the men of Punt.

3 they needed Muriela to be Yelaya.

4 they talked of their armies of soldiers.

5 they were working for him.

6 they wanted to talk to him.

7 they paid him for his help.

8 he was their old enemy.

9 ~~they were friends.~~

GRAMMAR CHECK

Comparative adjectives

We add -er to make the comparative form of most short adjectives.

tall   taller

When short adjectives finish in consonant + y we change y to i and add -er.

lazy   lazier

When adjectives finish in a short vowel + a single consonant we double the last consonant and add -er.   *red   redder*

With longer adjectives (other 2 syllable adjectives, or adjectives with 3+ syllables) we put more before the adjective.   *solid   more solid*

We use comparative adjective + than when comparing two people.

Muriela is more worried than Conan.

5 Write comparative sentences about Gwarunga and Gorulga.

a (strong) ..... *Gwarunga is stronger than Gorulga.* .....

b (old) ....

c (angry) ....

d (tall) ....

e (thin) ....

f (dangerous) ....

g (heavy) ....

h (trusting) ....

6 Write comparative sentences about Tutmekri and Zargeba.

a (lucky) Tutmekri is .... *luckier* .... than Zargeba.

b (fat) ....

c (young) ....

d (strong) ....

e (hairy) ....

f (careful) ....

g (short) ....

GRAMMAR CHECK

Past Simple information questions

We use question words (how, who, what, why, when, and where) in information questions. We answer these questions with information. With the verb be, the word order is question word + be + subject.

Who was Bît-Yakin? A wizard from Asgalun.

With other verbs, we put an auxiliary verb before the subject.

How could Bît-Yakin speak as the oracle? Through holes in the wall.

After the auxiliary verb + subject, we use infinitive without *to*.

Why did Bît-Yakin come to Alkmeenon? To work for Yelaya.

7 **Complete each question about Bît-Yakin's servants with a word in the box. Match the answers below with the questions.**

how	how	what	what	when	where	where	who	who	why

a ......What...... were their eyes like? ☑

b .... could they talk to each other? ☐

c .... did they come to Alkmeenon? ☐

d .... was there all over their bodies? ☐

e .... did they kill in the lotus thicket? ☐

f .... did they put Bît-Yakin's dead body? ☐

g .... did they try to kill Conan in the tunnel? ☐

h .... did they hang from ladders over the river? ☐

i .... did they leave Muriela a prisoner in chains? ☐

j .... was the only man that could stop them killing people? ☐

1 Zargeba

2 gray fur

3 Bît-Yakin

4 cold and blue

5 using animal cries

6 hundreds of years ago

7 on the knees of a statue

8 in a cave in the blue cliffs

9 to catch dead bodies to eat

10 by dropping a stone on him

GRAMMAR CHECK

Reflexive pronouns

We use reflexive pronouns (myself, yourself, himself, herself, itself, ourselves, yourselves, and themselves) when the subject and the object of a verb are the same.

The ape-men and the wizard hid themselves from visitors.

By magic, Bît-Yakin stopped himself from becoming old.

We can also use reflexive pronouns to emphasize who did something, or for things that a person does alone without anybody else.

The servants themselves stayed in Alkmeenon.

You yourself spoke the oracle's words.

8 **Read Muriela's diary text about her time in Alkmeenon. Complete it with the words in the box.**

> herself   himself   himself   itself   ~~myself~~   myself
> ourselves   themselves   yourself   yourselves

I've often said to **a)** ....myself.... that I'm lucky. Conan
b) .... knew who I was when we met in Alkmeenon. I was
wearing the clothes of the great Oracle, Yelaya **c)** ...., and
speaking in a deep voice. But my voice **d)** .... told Conan
that I was from Corinthia. Then he remembered Zargeba, the slave
market, and my name. We slaves don't usually see **e)** .... as
important people, but Conan recognized me! Of course, the priests
f) .... thought that I was really Yelaya — until Gwarunga,
speaking **g)** .... as the oracle, told them not to believe my
words. Zargeba and Gwarunga, you wanted to make **h)** ....
rich, but now you're both dead. Isn't life strange? When nobody helps
you, helping **i)** .... isn't easy. But with Conan's help, I've
learned to believe in **j)** ....

GRAMMAR CHECK

Tag endings with different tenses

We use question tags to check information, or to ask someone to agree with us. The tag contains subject + main verb or auxiliary verb to match the sentence. When the sentence is affirmative, the question tag is negative. When the sentence is negative, the question tag is affirmative.

You can help me, can't you?   *We can't stay here, can we?*

With most tenses, we repeat the main or auxiliary verb in the question tag.

He was a wizard, wasn't he?   *She's an oracle, isn't she?*

It hasn't finished, has it?   *They won't kill us, will they?*

The negative tag for I am is irregular.   *I'm a fighter, aren't I?*

With affirmative Present or Past Simple verbs we use do or did in the question tag.

You want the jewels, don't you?   *We came here for them, didn't we?*

9 **What did Conan say to Muriela? Complete the sentences with tag endings.**

a They're ugly,... *aren't they*...?

b You don't feel afraid,..........................?

c They didn't hurt you,..........................?

d You can walk,..........................?

e I'm going to help you,..........................?

f You'll be OK,..........................?

10 **What did Muriela say to Conan? Use the prompts to make sentences.**

a they / have killed / all the priests
   They've killed all the priests, haven't they..........................?

b we / will / escape
   ....?

c I / must / not / look down
   ....?

d they / be / not / going to / follow us
   ....?

e we / can / reach / Punt quickly
   ....?

DOMINOES Your Choice

Read *Dominoes* for pleasure, or to develop language skills. It's your choice.

Each *Domino* reader includes:
- a good story to enjoy
- integrated activities to develop reading skills and increase vocabulary
- task-based projects – perfect for CEFR portfolios
- contextualized grammar activities

Each *Domino* pack contains a reader, and an excitingly dramatized audio recording of the story

If you liked this *Domino*, read these:

V is for Vampire
Lesley Thompson

'He's great, Vera,' said Angie.
When Viktor Sarav takes a job at Ballantine's, Angie and her brother Don – the young owners of the New York fashion company – are pleased. But soon there are strange deaths in the company. Is there a vampire at work at Ballantine's? Vera Donato, a company director with secrets to hide, is against Viktor. But Ed Valdemar, the company lawyer, trusts him. Who is right?

War Horse
Michael Morpurgo

'We'll be friends, you and I. I'll call you Joey,' Albert said. 'I'll look after you. We'll always be friends, I promise.'
Albert Narracott, a farmer's boy, makes this promise to his horse, Joey, in Devon, England. But this is before the First World War, and before Joey leaves for France to become a war horse. What happens to Joey in the British army? What will the Germans and the French do to him when they find him? And how will Albert find Joey again?

	CEFR	Cambridge Exams	IELTS	TOEFL iBT	TOEIC
Level 3	B1	PET	4.0	57-86	550
Level 2	A2–B1	KET-PET	3.0-4.0	–	390
Level 1	A1–A2	YLE Flyers/KET	3.0	–	225
Starter & Quick Starter	A1	YLE Movers	1.0–2.0	–	–

You can find details and a full list of books and teachers' resources on our website:
www.oup.com/elt/gradedreaders